# The Best Of Alex 2004

## Charles Peattie & Russell Taylor

Masterley Publishing

# The Best Of
# Alex
## 2004

FTSE Group is a proud supporter of Alex. Like our indices he is a measure of the fortunes within the financial and wider communities.
We're all hoping he has a great 2005!

MondoVisione, publisher of the Handbook of World Stock, Derivative and Commodity Exchanges, is pleased to support once more that other essential handbook of the financial community, the Alex annual.

# FOREWORD

Our thanks, as ever, to our spies in the City, who we depend on for stories.

In these times of spin and counter-spin, of rumours, gossip, leaks, lies, and deliberate misinformation we have to sift through countless different confusing and contradictory reports, never knowing who to trust.

Sometimes it may be necessary for us to change crucial details of the information out of a desire to protect the identity of our sources. And from time to time the information itself may have become distorted in the process. Occasionally, frankly, we get it wrong. It happens.

But in the end we can only say: by all means question our judgment, but please don't question our integrity.

Because we haven't got any. It's our job to be opportunistic and we constantly need new material.

So keep sending it in. All suggestions gratefully received, whether it's over lunch or over cyberspace (that's what your hotmail account's for after all). We understand many of you now habitually send work emails from your Blackberries while sitting on the loo at home. So, since this is the traditional place for Alex collections to be kept, our contact details, which are to be found on the inside back page of the book, should be within handy reach (we're guessing that's where you're reading this now).

We must admit we do sometimes wonder why you are so willing to let us in on your expense account wheezes and other scams, knowing that we will then feature them in a cartoon which will probably be read by your boss. We can only assume you like a challenge, or that you have the mindset of those James Bond villains who simply cannot resist taunting 007 in advance about the sheer fiendish ingenuity of their scheme to precipitate World War Three and achieve total domination etc, because they are so confident no one can stop them.

And it's true, we're not here to stop you. As professional satirists obviously we thoroughly disapprove of all forms of corporate greed. But we've got our livelihoods to consider too. Let's hope you keep getting away with it.

*Charles Peattie    Russell Taylor*

Charles Peattie and Russell Taylor

The story so far...

 **Alex** has been sacked from his job at investment bank Megabank by head of corporate finance

**Rupert**

He has found work as a client liaison officer for ghastly Northern metal basher

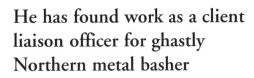 **Mr Hardcastle**

In the meantime Alex's ex-colleague **Clive**

(also a victim of the job cull at Megabank) has been working as Alex's chauffeur, much to the displeasure of his scary wife

 **Bridget**

Will Alex find another job in the City to provide for his wife

**Penny**

and son

 **Christopher?**

Now read on...

**Alex** FEATTIE + TAYLOR
DRIVING A MINICAB COULD BE SEEN AS SOMETHING OF A COME DOWN FOR AN EX-BANKER LIKE ME.

BUT IF ONE KEEPS ONE'S EYES AND EARS OPEN ONE CAN USE ONE'S INSIDE KNOWLEDGE OF BANKING TO GLEAN USEFUL INFORMATION...

FOR EXAMPLE, FROM THE DESTINATION THAT BUSINESS PASSENGERS ASK ME TO TAKE THEM TO I CAN OFTEN MAKE INFERENCES AS TO THE DEALS THEY'RE DOING...

STANSTED AIRPORT, PLEASE, DRIVER... ...OH GOD... IT'S YOU, CLIVE...

STANSTED? OH DEAR... REDUCED TO FLYING BUDGETJET? HAS BUSINESS GOT THAT BAD?

---

**Alex** FEATTIE + TAYLOR
SOMEONE LEAKED THE FACT THAT WE'RE FIRING FIFTY PEOPLE TODAY TO THE F.T.

AS A RESULT THEY'VE SPLASHED THE STORY ON THE FRONT PAGE AND WE'VE HAD A PROCESSION OF TERRIFIED EMPLOYEES COMING INTO WORK CONVINCED THEY'RE FOR THE CHOP.

OH WELL, SHELLEY, WE'D BETTER GET STARTED. CALL GUS CARR IN AND TELL HIM HE'S BEING FIRED FOR HIS GENERAL LACK OF APPLICATION TO HIS JOB...

ER...BUT, RUPERT, HE'S NOT ON THE LIST...

NO, BUT HE WAS THE ONLY ONE WHO LOOKED RELAXED THIS MORNING. HE CLEARLY DOESN'T BOTHER TO READ THE FINANCIAL PAGES ON THE TRAIN...

---

**Alex** FEATTIE + TAYLOR
FOR GOODNESS' SAKE, ALEX, PULL YOURSELF TOGETHER. YOU'VE GOT NO JOB BUT IT'S NOT THE END OF THE WORLD.

LIKE YOU, I NEVER DREAMT WE'D BE OUT OF WORK THIS LONG BUT AT LEAST I PUT A BRAVE FACE ON IT AND KEEP MY COMPOSURE IN PUBLIC...

BUT LOOK AT YOU... FORLORN, DEPRESSED, WITHDRAWN, PRE-OCCUPIED, TENSE AND RATTY... WHAT IMPRESSION DO YOU THINK THAT GIVES OTHER PEOPLE?

WELL, HOPEFULLY THAT I'M IN EMPLOYMENT AND SUFFERING FROM STANDARD PRE-BONUS ANXIETY SYNDROME.

OOPS. GOOD IDEA. I FORGOT ABOUT THAT...

---

**Alex** FEATTIE + TAYLOR
JUST A MONTH TO GO TILL THAT TRAGIC DAY WHEN CONCORDE GOES OUT OF SERVICE FOREVER.

THE THOUGHT THAT THERE WILL NO LONGER BE SUPERSONIC AIR TRAVEL ACROSS THE ATLANTIC COMES AS A DEVASTATING BLOW TO SENIOR EXECUTIVES LIKE MYSELF...

IT'S CATASTROPHIC... I CAN'T BRING MYSELF TO IMAGINE WHAT LIFE IS GOING TO BE LIKE...

WELL, RUPERT, I IMAGINE LIFE WILL JUST GO ON PRETTY MUCH AS NORMAL.

EXACTLY. AND ALL THE CLIENTS I USED TO BILL MY CONCORDE FLIGHTS TO, CITING "URGENT BUSINESS NECESSITY" WILL REALISE THEY WASTED THEIR MONEY...

# Alex

**FEATTIE + TAYLOR**

DRIVING YOUR CAB MUST GIVE YOU AN INSIGHT INTO THE MOOD IN THE CITY, CLIVE...

IT DOES

I PICK UP A LOT OF THE CHAPS FROM CONTINENT BANK AND FROM THE AMOUNT THEY TIP ME I CAN TELL HOW CONFIDENT THEY FEEL ABOUT THEIR FUTURE...

SOME NEVER GIVE ME ANYTHING, SOME THE ODD FIVER, WHEREAS ONE CHAP ALWAYS HANDS ME A £20 NOTE. YOU CAN SEE HOW SECURE *HE* FEELS IN HIS JOB...

YES...

HE'S UTTERLY PARANOID ABOUT BEING FIRED, CLEARLY...

YES. HENCE HIM BRIBING ME TO KEEP HIM UP TO SPEED ON ANY REDUNDANCIES RUMOURS I'VE PICKED UP...

*email: alex-cartoon@etgate.co.uk*

---

# Alex

**FEATTIE + TAYLOR**

FOR PEOPLE LIKE OURSELVES - NOW APPROACHING MIDDLE AGE - FINDING JOBS IN BANKING CAN BE PROBLEMATIC...

OBVIOUSLY IT IS NOT ACCEPTED FORM FOR DIRECT QUESTIONS RELATING TO AGE TO BE ASKED IN AN INTERVIEW SITUATION.

BUT AN EDUCATED GUESS CAN USUALLY BE MADE WHICH MAY CAUSE INVOLUNTARY PREJUDICE TO SET IN ABOUT THE PERSON ACROSS THE TABLE...

YES...

SO, HOW OLD WOULD YOU SAY *YOUR* INTERVIEWER - AND PROSPECTIVE NEW BOSS - WAS?

NO MORE THAN 32... B*ST**D... IT'S SO DEPRESSING...

*email: alex-cartoon@etgate.co.uk*

---

# Alex

**FEATTIE + TAYLOR**

I SEE YOU'RE IN A SUIT TODAY, PETER.

YES. OUR BANK HAS ABANDONED ITS DRESS DOWN FRIDAYS...

BUSINESS IS BAD AND IT'S DEEMED BETTER FOR THE BANK'S IMAGE FOR ITS STAFF TO BE SMARTLY DRESSED AT WORK...

THE WISDOM OF MANAGEMENT...

QUITE. AFTER ALL, WHAT IMPRESSION WOULD IT CREATE TO A VISITING POTENTIAL CLIENT TO SEE TRADERS SPORTING PONY TAILS AND SCRUFFY CASUAL CLOTHES?

WELL, THAT THEY MUST BE MAKING LOTS OF MONEY FOR THEIR BANK TO BE ABLE TO GET AWAY WITH SUCH AN ICONOCLASTIC IMAGE?

EXACTLY. WHEREAS *NOW* WE LOOK LIKE TOTAL CONFORMIST LOSERS...

*email: alex-cartoon@etgate.co.uk*

---

# Alex

**FEATTIE + TAYLOR**

IT SEEMS THAT ALL MY FRIENDS THINK I'M UTTERLY USELESS AT EVERYTHING I TURN MY HAND TO...

TAKE MY LATEST PLAN:- TO USE THE FACT THAT I'M UNEMPLOYED TO WRITE A BLOCKBUSTER THRILLER BASED ON MY EXPERIENCES IN THE CITY...

WHEN I PHONED EVERYONE TO TELL THEM OF MY AMBITIONS TO BE AN AUTHOR, THEIR RESPONSE WAS MOST DISCOURAGING...

THEY ALL SAY IT'S A REALLY GOOD IDEA...

OH DEAR...SO THEY'RE NOT QUAKING IN THEIR BOOTS AND OFFERING YOU JOBS TO STOP YOU UNMASKING THEIR CORPORATE SHENANIGANS?

*email: alex-cartoon@etgate.co.uk*

**Alex** PEATTIE + TAYLOR

NEW REGULATORY CODES MAY OBLIGE CLIENTS TO PAY FOR RESEARCH WRITTEN BY THE BANK'S ANALYSTS LIKE YOU, ROBERT...

AND THE FEELING IS THAT MOST FUND MANAGERS WOULDN'T BOTHER.

RIDICULOUS. HOW CAN THEY MAKE KEY BUSINESS DECISIONS WITHOUT THE NECESSARY INFORMATION?

WE NEED TO STRESS TO THEM THE IMPORTANCE OF BEING IN POSSESSION OF THE RELEVANT DATA, STATISTICAL ANALYSIS, CHARTS AND GRAPHS.

I'M GLAD YOU FEEL THAT WAY...

BECAUSE I'M THINKING OF SUBSCRIBING TO THIS SERVICE THAT RATES CITY ANALYSTS ON HOW CORRECT THEIR RECOMMENDATIONS HAVE BEEN.

OH... THAT?... ≡AHEM≡ TOTAL WASTE OF MONEY...

email: alex-cartoon@etgate.co.uk

---

**Alex** PEATTIE + TAYLOR

HOW WAS YOUR JOB INTERVIEW TODAY, CLIVE?

IT WENT REALLY WELL ACTUALLY...

WE DIDN'T ACTUALLY TALK BUSINESS AT ALL. THE INTERVIEWER TURNED OUT TO BE A BIG RUGBY FAN SO WE JUST CHATTED ABOUT SPORT...

WELL IT'S ALWAYS GOOD TO BOND...

ANYWAY HE REALLY LIKED ME AND AT THE END OF THE INTERVIEW HE ASKED ME WHEN I COULD START WORK AND I SAID "TOMORROW"!

SO YOU'RE WAITING TO HEAR BACK..?

SO, THAT CANDIDATE CLIVE? YOU WANT ME TO SEND HIM A REJECTION LETTER?

RUGBY FIXTURES

YES. WHAT RIGHT-MINDED UNEMPLOYED PERSON WOULD WANT TO WALK INTO A JOB NOW WITH 2 MONTHS OF RUGBY COMING UP ON THE TELLY?

email: alex-cartoon@etgate.co.uk

---

**Alex** PEATTIE + TAYLOR

WE'VE JUST GOT THE DRAFT NUMBERS FOR THE BANK'S THIRD QUARTER PROFITABILITY...

I'M AFRAID THEY MAKE GRIM READING FOR HEADS OF DEPARTMENT LIKE US... THIS IS A DEVASTATING BLOW THAT COULDN'T HAVE COME AT A WORSE TIME...

I THINK WE'D BEST KEEP THESE FIGURES TO OURSELVES, DAVID. RELEASING THEM COULD HAVE A VERY DETRIMENTAL EFFECT ON OFFICE MORALE... YES...

...IF WORD GOT OUT THAT BUSINESS IS PICKING UP...

EVERYONE'S BONUS EXPECTATIONS WOULD SUDDENLY GO SKY-HIGH....

email: alex-cartoon@etgate.co.uk

---

**Alex** PEATTIE + TAYLOR

ALEX IS DOING SOME WORK AS A FREELANCE BUSINESS CONSULTANT...

WHY DON'T WE HAVE THE MEETING OVER DINNER?

HIS RECENT EXPERIENCE OF WORKING FOR HARDCASTLE HAS MADE HIS SERVICES HIGHLY PRIZED.

SHALL WE SAY "LE GOURMET"? BE SURE TO BOOK A WINDOW TABLE...

ESPECIALLY AMONG BANKS WHO HAVE NOT BEEN SUCCESSFUL IN PITCHES TO INDUSTRIAL COMPANIES RECENTLY.

SEND A CAR TO PICK ME UP AT 7:30 PLEASE

I TRUST YOU ARRANGED THE LAP-DANCING FOR AFTERWARDS AS REQUESTED.

ER... SO WHEN DO YOU TELL US WHY WE DIDN'T WIN HARDCASTLE'S ACCOUNT?

YOU MEAN YOU HAVEN'T GUESSED YET?

email: alex-cartoon@etgate.co.uk

**Alex** PEATTIE + TAYLOR

SO WHAT ARE YOUR CHANCES OF FINDING WORK IN BANKING AGAIN, ALEX?

REASONABLY PROMISING ACTUALLY...

OF COURSE ONCE UPON A TIME THEY WOULDN'T HAVE BEEN SO GOOD BUT OVER RECENT YEARS MANY ORGANISATIONS HAVE BEEN FORCED TO IMPLEMENT "DIVERSITY" QUOTAS...

BANKS HAVING TO EMPLOY A BROADER RANGE OF PEOPLE FROM THE VARIOUS MINORITIES SHOULD WORK TO MY ADVANTAGE...

BUT, ALEX, YOU'RE A WHITE MIDDLE-CLASS MAN...

ER...YES. I'M PINNING MY HOPES ON GETTING SIX MONTHS' WORK AS MATERNITY LEAVE COVER FOR SOME TOKEN FEMALE BANKER...

I SEE... SO YOU'RE TOTALLY DESPERATE...

email: alex-cartoon@etgate.co.uk

**Alex** PEATTIE + TAYLOR

BEING AN ANALYST IS NO LONGER THE GLAMOROUS JOB IT WAS A FEW YEARS AGO...

BACK THEN THEY COULD EARN A FORTUNE PUFFING DOTCOM STOCKS OR TAKING BACKHANDERS FROM THEIR BANKING DIVISION TO TALK UP CORPORATE CLIENTS' SHARE PRICES.

SADLY FOR THEM, DEPRESSED STOCK MARKETS AND NEW FINANCIAL REGULATIONS HAVE PUT PAID TO THAT SORT OF SELF-INTERESTED NEST-FEATHERING...

YES...

...SO IT'S BACK TO THE OLD SORT...

YES, I'M A LEISURE ANALYST AGAIN THESE DAYS...

SO YOU SPEND YOUR DAY VISITING BREWERIES, HOTELS AND GOLF COURSES?

email: alex-cartoon@etgate.co.uk

**Alex** PEATTIE + TAYLOR

HOW WAS THE OCTOBER CLUB DINNER, CLIVE? I HOPE YOU DIDN'T BUY ANY OF THOSE OVERPRICED CHARITY AUCTION ITEMS...

NOT THIS YEAR, BRIDGET. I'M AWARE THAT WE'VE GOT NO MONEY. AND FRANKLY I THINK A LOT OF OTHER PEOPLE WERE IN THE SAME POSITION...

REALLY?

OH YES. AUCTION PRICES WERE NOTICEABLY WELL DOWN ON PREVIOUS YEARS. THE DAY'S CHALK STREAM FISHING THAT I USUALLY BUY ONLY WENT FOR A MISERLY £250...

£250...?

THAT'S WHAT YOU TOLD ME YOU PAID FOR IT LAST YEAR...

ER... DID I? I MEAN... OH GOD...

email: alex-cartoon@etgate.co.uk

**Alex** PEATTIE + TAYLOR

SO WHAT'S THE STORY ON CORPORATE DEALS THESE DAYS, JEREMY? ANYTHING GOING ON?

WELL, EVERYONE'S VERY EXCITED ABOUT RUSSIA, ALEX. THESE NEW SO-CALLED "OIL-IGARCHS" ARE OPENING UP THEIR COUNTRY'S HUGE NATURAL WEALTH TO WESTERN INVESTORS...

BANKERS HAVE BEEN ENTHUSING ABOUT THE SIZE AND CAPACITY OF OILFIELDS OUT THERE FOR AGES. WE'RE TALKING OF SOME AMAZINGLY LONG PIPELINES...

WHAT, THE ONES EVERYONE CLAIMS THAT THEIR DEALS ARE IN?

YES... TRANS-SIBERIAN, JUDGING BY THE TIME IT'S TAKING FOR ANYTHING ACTUALLY TO EMERGE...

email: alex-cartoon@etgate.co.uk

**Alex** PEATTIE + TAYLOR

MELANIE, WOULD YOU MIND STEPPING INTO THE MEETING ROOM WITH ME PLEASE...

OTHERWISE IT WOULD JUST BE SUE AND MYSELF IN THERE WHICH WOULD CONTRAVENE THE BANK'S GUIDELINES ON AVOIDING THE POSSIBILITY OF SEXUAL HARASSMENT.

BEING LEFT ALONE TOGETHER COULD GIVE RISE TO A SITUATION WHERE ONE PARTY MIGHT FEEL VULNERABLE TO UNWELCOME PERSISTENT ATTENTIONS FROM THE OTHER...

OF COURSE...

IT'S BONUS TIME COMING UP...

AND THE LAST THING I WANT IS HER BENDING MY EAR ABOUT HOW HARD SHE'S BEEN WORKING ALL YEAR...

**Alex** PEATTIE + TAYLOR

SO THAT CANDIDATE FOR THE POST OF OPTIONS TRADER:- HOW DID HE SHAPE UP?

WELL WE GAVE HIM A PRETTY INTENSIVE GRILLING.

A WHOLE AFTERNOON OF BACK-TO-BACK INTERVIEWS WITH VARIOUS TEAM MEMBERS... HIS THEORETICAL GRASP OF THE SUBJECT WAS PRETTY GOOD...

BUT I'M AFRAID TOWARDS THE END HE RAISED HIS HAND AND ASKED A QUESTION WHICH CAUSED US IMMEDIATELY TO RULE HIM OUT OF CONTENTION.

WHAT DID HE ASK?

"COULD I GO TO THE LOO PLEASE?"

OH DEAR... IF YOU'RE RUNNING A $200M POSITION AND THE MARKET CAN MOVE AGAINST YOU AT ANY MINUTE YOU NEED A CAST IRON BLADDER.

**Alex** PEATTIE + TAYLOR

TIME'S SLIPPING ME BY, PENNY... I'VE BEEN OUT OF THE CITY FOR OVER SIX MONTHS NOW...

CONVENTIONAL WISDOM HOLDS THAT ONE CAN ONLY SPEND A YEAR TO 18 MONTHS OUT OF THE MARKET BEFORE ONE BECOMES UNEMPLOYABLE AS A BANKER...

I CAN ALREADY FEEL HOW I'M STARTING TO LOSE THOSE ESSENTIAL ATTRIBUTES THAT MAKE A TOP CORPORATE FINANCIER...

MARKET SHARPNESS? BUSINESS NOUS?

NO, ADVANCE RESERVATIONS AT THE IVY. I HAD TO CANCEL ANOTHER ONE TODAY DUE TO NO LONGER HAVING AN EXPENSE ACCOUNT...

**Alex** PEATTIE + TAYLOR

WE'RE REALLY MISSING HAVING A BANKER OF THE CALIBRE OF ALEX AT THIS YEAR'S MILK ROUND...

MEGA-BANK RECEPTION

THE CHAPS WE'VE BROUGHT ALONG ARE QUITE ADEQUATE, BUT THEY DON'T INSPIRE STUDENTS OR MOTIVATE THEM TO WANT TO COME AND WORK FOR US LIKE ALEX DID...

HE JUST HAD AN INSTINCTIVE ABILITY TO COMMUNICATE THE EXCITEMENT, THE GLAMOUR AND THE SHEER SEXINESS OF BANKING TO YOUNG PEOPLE...

YES... I REMEMBER LAST YEAR...

HE IGNORED THEM ALL AND SPENT THE WHOLE EVENING TAKING BUSINESS CALLS ON HIS MOBILE AND CHECKING HIS BLACKBERRY...

MAYBE I WAS WRONG TO FIRE HIM...

email: alex-cartoon@etgate.co.uk

**Alex** PEATTIE + TAYLOR

IT CAN BE TOUGH GOING TO THE LEAVING DO OF AN EMPLOYEE YOU'VE HAD TO MAKE REDUNDANT.

THE HARDEST BIT IS EXPLAINING THAT THE DECISION IN NO WAY REFLECTS THE PROFESSIONAL COMPETENCE OF THE PERSON WHO'S BEEN FIRED...

TO CUT COSTS HEAD OFFICE WILL HAVE DECREED THAT A CERTAIN POSITION IS TO DISAPPEAR... YET SOME PEOPLE SEEM UNABLE TO BE DISPASSIONATE AND ACCEPT THIS FACT...

I REPEAT: THERE IS NO JOB GOING AT MEGABANK... NOW WILL YOU ALL PLEASE GO AND TALK TO KEANE...

STEVE KEANE'S LEAVING DRINKS

**Alex** PEATTIE + TAYLOR

I'M GOING TO MY BEAUTICIAN FOR BOTOX TREATMENT. AFTER ALL IT'S THAT TIME OF YEAR...

BONUS TIME. AND WOMEN FREQUENTLY RECEIVE LOWER LEVELS OF PAYOUTS THAN THEIR MALE COUNTERPARTS.

TRUE, BUT IS THIS THE RIGHT RESPONSE, SUE?

TRYING TO EXTORT A BIGGER BONUS OUT OF YOUR MALE BOSS BY PANDERING TO A STEREOTYPE OF FEMALE ATTRACTIVENESS?

I JUST WANT TO LOOK RIGHT ON THE DAY.

DID YOU SEE HOW SHE LOOKED? NOT A FLICKER OF EMOTION...TOTALLY DEADPAN...

MAYBE WE DIDN'T OFFER HER ENOUGH...

WORRY    FRET    FROZEN

BOTOX CLINIC

BILL

BILL

**Alex** PEATTIE + TAYLOR

IT'S TRADITIONAL CITY PRACTICE FOR PEOPLE TO TIME THEIR BUSINESS TRIPS ABROAD TO COINCIDE WITH ATTENDING SPORTING FIXTURES THERE...

IN MY CASE, I'M TRYING TO SET UP JOB INTERVIEWS IN SYDNEY WHICH CONVENIENTLY OCCUR DURING THE RUGBY WORLD CUP. IT'S THE PERFECT EXCUSE...

AH! I SEE, BECAUSE BY DOING INTERVIEWS IN AUSTRALIA ONE CAN WRITE OFF ONE'S TRIP TO THE RUGBY AGAINST TAX?

THAT'S CERTAINLY TRUE...

BUT MORE IMPORTANTLY IT STOPS PEOPLE REALISING I'M NOW SERIOUSLY CONSIDERING TAKING A JOB DOWN UNDER AT ½ LONDON SALARY LEVELS...

B****CKS TO THE RUGBY... I'M GETTING DESPERATE, CLIVE...

email: alex-cartoon@etgate.co.uk

---

**Alex** PEATTIE + TAYLOR

ARE YOU GOING TO HAVE YOUR FLU JAB AT LUNCHTIME?

OH YES... I ALWAYS DO...

I HATE NEEDLES BUT IT'S A RESPONSIBLE ACT TO TAKE ADVANTAGE OF THE FREE WINTER INOCULATIONS PROVIDED BY THE BANK...

ONE ONLY HAS TO THINK OF THE SERIOUS FINANCIAL RAMIFICATIONS FOR OUR EMPLOYER IF YOU OR I FELL ILL AND WAS UNABLE TO COME INTO WORK...

AND WEREN'T AT OUR DESKS AT THE PSYCHOLOGICALLY IMPORTANT TIME WHEN THE BONUSES ARE BEING WORKED OUT?

QUITE...THEY MIGHT TRY NOT TO PAY US ONE...

email: alex-cartoon@etgate.co.uk

---

**Alex** PEATTIE + TAYLOR

AFTER ALMOST A YEAR OUT OF WORK ALEX IS OBVIOUSLY PLAYING DOWN THE IMPORTANCE OF A BANKING CAREER.

I DON'T KNOW ABOUT YOU, MIKE, BUT I FOUND THE CITY HAD STOPPED BEING FUN ANY MORE. THERE WERE NONE OF THE CHARACTERS, NO MORE LONG LUNCHES...

AND FRANKLY IF YOU DON'T NEED THE MONEY WHAT'S THE POINT IN PUTTING IN THOSE PUNISHING HOURS?

SO HAS ALEX SAVED ENOUGH NOT TO HAVE TO WORK ANY MORE?

NO, BUT HE'S HOPING MIKE HAS...

HAVEN'T YOU BEEN TEMPTED TO JACK IT ALL IN?

RIGHT NOW, BANKS ARE REALLY ONLY RECRUITING WHEN SOMEONE RETIRES...

email: alex-cartoon@etgate.co.uk

---

**Alex** PEATTIE + TAYLOR

=SIGH= IF I HAD A JOB I'D BE LOBBYING HARD FOR MY BONUS NOW...

WELL THAT'S NO GREAT LOSS...

AFTER ALL YOUR LAST TWO YEARS' BONUSES WERE ALWAYS PALTRY DESPITE YOU HAVING PUT IN ALL THAT "FACE TIME" IN YOUR OFFICE TO PROVE YOU WERE TAKING YOUR WORK SERIOUSLY...

IMAGINE WHAT IT WOULD BE LIKE RIGHT NOW IF YOU WERE FORCED TO PULL OUT ALL THE STOPS TO MAKE SURE YOU WERE CONSTANTLY UNDER YOUR BOSS'S EYE...

ER...YES...

LOOKING FORWARD TO THE RUGBY, ALEX?

VERY MUCH. WHAT TIME DO WE GET INTO SYDNEY?

ZZZ... =SIGH=

email: alex-cartoon@etgate.co.uk

**Row 1**

**Alex** — PEATTIE + TAYLOR

MY FIRST ACT AS A HEADHUNTER WAS TO PLACE A BOGUS AD IN THE FINANCIAL PRESS...

IT OFFERED A SENIOR JOB AT A LUDICROUSLY HIGH SALARY... LOTS OF PEOPLE SENT IN THEIR RESUMÉS WHICH I CAN NOW TOUT AROUND THE MARKET.

VERY SNEAKY...

PAT

YES, BUT IT'S BRINGING IN THE BUSINESS... IN FACT I COULD USE AN ASSISTANT. WOULD YOU BE INTERESTED IN THE JOB, CLIVE?

ABSOLUTELY. SHOULD I PUT IN A FORMAL APPLICATION?

NO NEED. I'VE ALREADY GOT YOUR C.V. ... SO YOU FANCIED YOURSELF AS "HEAD OF M+A AT A LEADING U.S. INVESTMENT BANK AT £750 K"

THAT WAS YOU? BLAST...

email: alex-cartoon@etgate.co.uk

**Row 2**

**Alex** — PEATTIE + TAYLOR

WHAT TIME ARE YOU LUNCHING THAT JOB CANDIDATE ALEX? SHOULDN'T YOU BE LEAVING?

I'M CALLING HIS OFFICE NOW...

HELLO? MIKE DAW'S PHONE.

HI I'M SUPPOSED TO BE HAVING LUNCH WITH MIKE TODAY. COULD YOU CONFIRM THE DETAILS?

I'LL LOOK IN HIS DIARY... OH YES... "LUNCH: ALEX MASTERLEY; LE GOURMET. 1 PM..."

GOOD...THANKS VERY MUCH... 'BYE...

CLICK

ER...ALEX...SO SHOULDN'T YOU BE LEAVING?

NO POINT...

IF HE'S OPENLY WRITTEN MY NAME IN HIS DIARY HE'S CLEARLY JUST USING THIS AS A WAY TO WANGLE A BIGGER BONUS OUT OF HIS BOSS...

email: alex-cartoon@etgate.co.uk

**Row 3**

**Alex** — PEATTIE + TAYLOR

HELLO... IT'S ALEX MASTERLEY...THERE'S GOOD NEWS ABOUT THAT CANDIDATE I'M RECRUITING FOR YOU...

HEAD OF DEPT.

YOU KNOW YOU WERE WORRIED THAT WHEN HE RESIGNED FROM HIS OLD BANK THEY WOULD ENFORCE A PERIOD OF "GARDENING LEAVE" BEFORE HE COULD START WORK FOR YOU?

YES...

WELL IT'S ALL BEEN SORTED... I'VE ARRANGED THINGS SO THAT HE WILL BE FREE TO JOIN YOU IMMEDIATELY...

EXCELLENT. GOOD WORK, ALEX.

SO YOU DIDN'T MENTION THAT THE CANDIDATE GOT FIRED AFTER YOU ACCIDENTALLY E-MAILED HIS C.V. TO HIS OWN BOSS?

OR THAT THEY'RE BOTH CURRENTLY SUING US... NO.

email: alex-cartoon@etgate.co.uk

**Row 4**

**Alex** — PEATTIE + TAYLOR

THEY SAY HEAD-HUNTERS ARE CYNICAL AND CALLOUS, BUT ALEX IS NOT LIKE THAT AT ALL...

ONE OF HIS CLIENTS JUST CALLED. HE'D BEEN SUMMONED INTO HIS BOSS'S OFFICE AT HIS BANK AND TOLD HE WAS BEING MADE REDUNDANT...

HE'D BEEN GIVEN JUST 15 MINUTES TO COLLECT HIS POSSESSIONS AND LEAVE... WELL, ALEX DROPPED EVERYTHING AND RUSHED OFF TO MEET HIM FOR A CONSOLATION DRINK...

SO HOW ABOUT FINDING ME A NEW JOB, ALEX?

NEVER MIND THAT... DID YOU SWIPE YOUR BANK'S INTERNAL PHONE DIRECTORY FOR ME LIKE I ASKED?

GIN LINE

RUMMAGE ROOT

email: alex-cartoon@etgate.co.uk

**Alex** PEATTIE + TAYLOR

JOHN BAIN BRIDGE'S RETIREMENT PARTY

COMING UP TO RETIREMENT A LOT OF PEOPLE MIGHT BE TEMPTED TO SLACK OFF...

YOU KNOW: TAKE IT EASY WORK-WISE, LET THINGS SLIDE A BIT, GET INTO THE OFFICE LATE, SHUFFLE A FEW PAPERS AT YOUR DESK, GO HOME EARLY... BUT NOT JOHN...

HE'S SHOWN A COMMENDABLE PROFESSIONAL ATTITUDE AND OVER RECENT MONTHS HAS INFLICTED A MORE PUNISHING WORK SCHEDULE ON HIMSELF THAN EVER...

ABSOLUTELY.

GRATUITOUS BUSINESS TRIPS TO MAURITIUS, HONG KONG, KOREA...

WELL HE HAD TO BUILD UP THE AIR MILES TO SEE HIM THROUGH HIS TWILIGHT YEARS...

---

**Alex** PEATTIE + TAYLOR

EVEN IF I SAY SO MYSELF I THINK I'M A PRETTY DAMN FINE HEADHUNTER...

OF COURSE MY SUCCESS IS REALLY JUST AN INDICATION OF HOW UP TO DATE MY CONTACTS ARE AND MY GENERAL STANDING IN THE FINANCIAL WORLD.

BUT, CLIVE, YOU GOT MADE REDUNDANT IN JANUARY AND YOU'VE BEEN OUT OF THE MARKET SITTING AT HOME FOR ALMOST A YEAR NOW...

EXACTLY.

NO CITY MAÎTRE D'S RECOGNISE ME ANY MORE AND JUST SHOW ME STRAIGHT TO A TABLE AT THE BACK BY THE LOOS...

AH YES... THE IDEAL PLACE FOR DISCREETLY LUNCHING A CANDIDATE...

---

**Alex** PEATTIE + TAYLOR

XMAS PARTY →

OF COURSE THE COMPLIANCE DIVISION OF A BANK IS NO LONGER THE BACKWATER IT ONCE WAS...

AS A RESULT OF THE VARIOUS CORPORATE SCANDALS OF RECENT YEARS ALL SORTS OF STRINGENT NEW LEGISLATION HAS BEEN INTRODUCED...

WHICH MEANS THAT PEOPLE LIKE NIGEL OVER THERE ARE NOW BIG PLAYERS WITHIN THE BANK WHO WIELD CONSIDERABLE POWER... YOU KNOW, I FANCY A DANCE... DO YOU THINK I SHOULD ASK HIM?

WHY NOT?

ER... NIGEL, COULD I HAVE A DANCE...? ER... WITH ANDREW HERE FROM OUR BANKING DIVISION?

HMM... THAT'S THE OTHER SIDE OF THE CHINESE WALL. I'LL HAVE TO REFER IT TO HEAD OFFICE...

---

**Alex** PEATTIE + TAYLOR

ALL THAT HASSLING OF OUR EX-BOSS RUPERT HAS PAID OFF. HE'S OFFERED ME A JOB AT MEGABANK.

WHAT?!

WELL IT'S JUST A DAY'S FREELANCE WORK AS AN EXTERNAL CONSULTANT BUT IT SOUNDS INTERESTING. HE'S GETTING ME IN TO THE BANK TO HOST A SERIES OF INFORMAL ONE-ON-ONE INTERVIEWS WITH INDIVIDUALS THERE.

I HAVE TO GET THEIR INPUT INTO HOW THEY RATE THEMSELVES, HOW SUCCESSFULLY THEY HAVE INTERACTED WITH THOSE AROUND THEM OVER THE YEAR AND RECOMMEND STRUCTURES FOR MOTIVATING AND REWARDING THEM.

I SEE...

SANTA'S GROTTO →

MEGABANK XMAS KIDS PARTY

ER... SO YOU'VE BEEN A GOOD BOY? AND WHAT WOULD YOU LIKE FROM SANTA?

CAR WASH TOKEN →

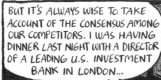

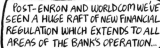

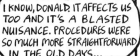

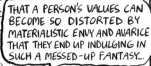

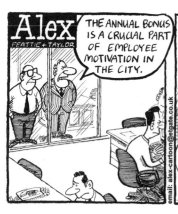

**Alex** PEATTIE + TAYLOR

ONCE UPON A TIME WE ANALYSTS WERE SUPERSTARS... NOWADAYS WE'RE NOBODIES...

IN THE POST-ENRON REGULATORY ENVIRONMENT WE'RE NO LONGER ALLOWED TO MAKE A FORTUNE FROM PUFFING OUR INVESTMENT BANKING CLIENTS' SHARE PRICES...

AND THESE DAYS MOST OF THE FUND MANAGERS HAVE THEIR OWN IN-HOUSE ANALYSTS, SO THEY NO LONGER NEED US EITHER...

THERE MUST BE SOME ROLE LEFT FOR YOU, TIM... WHAT SECTOR DO YOU COVER?

THE EQUITY SALES TEAM'S BOTTOMS.

TIM, I NEED SOME GUFF TO GIVE A CLIENT ABOUT HOW I WAS RIGHT AT THE TIME TO RECOMMEND A STOCK THAT SUBSEQUENTLY BOMBED...

---

**Alex** PEATTIE + TAYLOR

I THINK YOU'RE BEING UNDULY HARSH ON JACKSON, RUPERT...

HE LOST US £50M ON A DERIVATIVES PUNT...

TRUE, BUT WE IN SENIOR MANAGEMENT HAPPILY POCKET OUR SHARE OF THE INCREASED BONUS POOL WHEN OUR TRADERS MAKE MONEY, YET WHEN THINGS GO WRONG WE TURN ON THEM...

I'M JUST MAKING A CASE FOR YOU TO SHOW A LITTLE MORE COMPASSION; TO TREAT JACKSON IN AN APPROPRIATELY FAIR AND CIVILISED MANNER...

AND SACK HIM...

OH NO... I WANT HIM HERE TO TAKE THE FLAK FROM THE OTHER STAFF ONCE WE ANNOUNCE THE REDUCED BONUSES NEXT WEEK...

---

**Alex** PEATTIE + TAYLOR

YOU HEAR ABOUT OUR EQUITY SALES DESK? WE TRIED TO SACK HALF OF THEM BUT THE OTHER HALF THREATENED TO RESIGN IN PROTEST.

REALLY?

YES... THEY KNEW FULL WELL THAT WE'D BE FORCED TO REINSTATE THE SACKED TEAM MEMBERS IF THEY DID IT... IT WAS ANNOYING BUT I MUST SAY I ADMIRED THEIR PRINCIPLES...

AFTER ALL THEY'RE A CLOSE-KNIT TEAM AND I SUPPOSE IT ISN'T FAIR THAT ONE LOT SHOULD SUFFER A DISADVANTAGE WHILE THE OTHERS SHOULD BE REWARDED WITH A MEASURE OF SECURITY...

NO...

SO THEY WERE REALLY THAT MIFFED ABOUT THEIR FELLOW TEAM MEMBERS WALTZING OFF WITH REDUNDANCY PAY-OFFS WHILE THEY WERE STUCK HERE WITHOUT EVEN A SNIFF OF A BONUS?

THAT'S RIGHT.

GLOWER  GLARE  SEETHE

---

**Alex** PEATTIE + TAYLOR

LOOK, DARLING, THIS IS HARD FOR ME TO SAY BUT... WELL, IT'S A YEAR SINCE I LOST MY JOB IN THE CITY...

YES?

WELL, I THINK IT'S TIME WE BROACHED THE QUESTION OF WHETHER YOU SHOULD GO OUT TO WORK OR NOT...

SURELY YOU CAN'T BE SUGGESTING WE CHANGE OUR CURRENT ARRANGEMENT...

LOOK, IT WOULD JUST BE REALLY USEFUL IF YOU WERE ABLE TO MAKE A POSITIVE CONTRIBUTION TO THE HOUSEHOLD FINANCES...

BUT, DARLING, WHAT WOULD I DO?

OH I DON'T KNOW...

SIT AT HOME? WATCH T.V. ALL DAY...? I JUST CAN'T AFFORD TO BAIL OUT YOUR LOSS-MAKING DITSY LITTLE PRIVATE BUSINESS ANY MORE...

YOU'VE NEVER HAD ANY FAITH IN MY BABYWEAR MARKETING CAREER, HAVE YOU?

48

**Strip 1**

ALEX, IT'S NOT FAIR TREATING CHRISTOPHER AS YOUR SKIVVY...

IT'S LIKE WORK EXPERIENCE FOR HIM...

ALL YOU SEEM TO DO IS HAVE HIM DOING TEDIOUS OFFICE DOGSBODY TASKS AND BEING A DRUDGE AND RUNNING PERSONAL ERRANDS FOR YOU...

THAT'S WHAT GRADUATE TRAINEES DO, PENNY...

HE'S AN INNOCENT CHILD... HIS LIFE SHOULDN'T BE LIKE THAT... SURELY THERE'S SUPPOSED TO BE SOME FUN IN IT... SOME MOMENTS OF LIGHTHEARTED LAUGHTER AT LEAST...?

THERE'S PLENTY OF THAT, PENNY....

I'VE SENT HIM DOWN TO THE LIBRARY TO RESEARCH INDIAN RUBBER MINES AND WHEN HE GETS BACK THERE'S A MESSAGE TO PHONE MR C. LYON AT LONDON ZOO...

TEE HEE

**Strip 2**

ALEX, THIS WHOLE CONCEPT OF HAVING CHRISTOPHER AS YOUR GRADUATE TRAINEE... I'M NOT SURE YOU'RE DOING THE RIGHT THING...

WHAT'S THE PROBLEM?

THINK ABOUT IT... PAY SOME CONSIDERATION TO HOW YOU MIGHT BE EXPLOITING HIM HERE, JUST TREATING HIM LIKE HE'S THE OFFICE DOGSBODY...

HUH?

HE'S ONLY A KID, ALEX! HE'S FOURTEEN! HIS VOICE HASN'T EVEN BROKEN YET...

YOU'RE RIGHT.

HE CAN ANSWER MY PHONE FOR ME AND PRETEND TO BE MY SECRETARY.

PING

**Strip 3**

WHAT A MARVELLOUS IDEA OF YOURS IT WAS TO GET AWAY TO THE CARIBBEAN FOR A FORTNIGHT AT EASTER...

I'M SO EXCITED... I CAN'T WAIT TO TELL ALEX AND PENNY TONIGHT...

ER, DARLING, I'M NOT SURE THAT'S SUCH A GOOD IDEA... REMEMBER ALEX IS OUT OF WORK.

HE CAN'T AFFORD TO GO ON HOLIDAY HIMSELF AND HE MIGHT BE FEELING A LITTLE BITTER ABOUT THE SITUATION...

DON'T BE SILLY, GAVIN. I'M SURE HE'LL BE TOTALLY POSITIVE ABOUT OUR TRIP...

ER... YES... I'M SURE HE WILL...

BARBADOS? THE BEGINNING OF APRIL? LOVELY!

AND SO HANDY FOR THE 3RD TEST MATCH OUT THERE ...EH, GAVIN...?

WHAT?!

**Strip 4**

SO YOU'RE RUNNING THE LONDON MARATHON AGAIN THIS YEAR?

YES FOR OXFAM...

HAVING FALLEN ON HARD TIMES MYSELF OF LATE I'M MORE AWARE THAN EVER OF THE IMPORTANCE OF RAISING MONEY FOR GOOD CAUSES...

THE FINANCIAL COMMUNITY IS MAKING MONEY AGAIN BUT THERE'S A TENDENCY FOR THEM TO TURN A BLIND EYE AND IGNORE THE PLIGHT OF THE LESS FORTUNATE PEOPLE IN THE WORLD...

WHAT, UNEMPLOYED BANKERS LIKE YOURSELF?

EXACTLY AND THIS IS A GOOD RUSE TO GET THROUGH TO THEM ON THE PHONE AND THEN BEG THEM FOR A JOB...

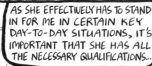

**Alex** PEATTIE + TAYLOR

SO, MIKE, I SEE YOU'VE GOT ONE OF THOSE SWANKY STATE OF THE ART IPOD DIGITAL MUSIC PLAYERS.

YUP.

I WISH I COULD AFFORD ONE - AREN'T YOU GOING TO USE THE SPECIAL EARPHONES THAT COME WITH IT?

THESE WHITE ONES?

NO. THEY'RE TOO DISTINCTIVE.

THEY ADVERTISE THE FACT THAT YOU'RE CARRYING SOME EXPENSIVE HARDWARE WHICH CAN ATTRACT MUGGERS. SO I USE THESE STANDARD HEADPHONES INSTEAD.

I SEE... IN THAT CASE...

ER...

PSST! IT'D BE EMBARRASSING FOR YOU IF YOU DID GET MUGGED AND THEY FIND YOU'VE JUST GOT THAT CHEAP WALKMAN...

WHITE EARPHONES

SHH... I'LL TAKE THAT RISK. MY SELF ESTEEM NEEDS A BOOST...

**Alex** PEATTIE + TAYLOR

I SEE THAT AIRLINES ARE STARTING TO INTRODUCE AN E-MAIL ACCESS FACILITY IN BUSINESS CLASS SEATS...

THIS IS A VERY USEFUL INNOVATION WHICH WILL BE INVALUABLE TO ORGANISATIONS LIKE OURS WHOSE EXECUTIVES DO A LOT OF BUSINESS TRAVEL...

ACTUALLY, RUPERT, MOST OF OUR PEOPLE ARE SO OVERWORKED THAT WHEN THEY GET ON A PLANE ALL THEY WANT TO DO IS SLEEP OR WATCH A MOVIE...

PRECISELY.

...AND THE ONLY PLACE WE NOW CAN'T KEEP TABS ON WHETHER THEY'RE WORKING IS ECONOMY CLASS... SO MAYBE THEY'LL FINALLY BE GRATEFUL THAT WE ALWAYS MAKE THEM FLY IT...

**Alex** PEATTIE + TAYLOR

FUNNY TO THINK THAT THE CITY OF LONDON STARTED ALL THOSE YEARS AGO WITH PEOPLE DOING DEALS IN COFFEE SHOPS...

IT'S COME A LONG WAY SINCE THEN. INSTEAD OF SMALL STOCKBROKERS WE NOW HAVE GLOBAL INVESTMENT BANKS...

AND THERE HAVE BEEN BOOMS AND BUSTS ALONG THE WAY..

YES. BUT NOW THE CITY'S PUT ITS HOUSE IN ORDER FOLLOWING THE DOTCOM CRASH AND THE SUBSEQUENT CORPORATE SCANDALS WE'RE ON THE VERGE OF A NEW UPTURN IN THE CYCLE...

YES.

WITH PEOPLE DOING DEALS IN COFFEE SHOPS...

WELL THANKS TO THE NEW REGULATIONS NONE OF THE DEPARTMENTS IN BANKS ARE OFFICIALLY ALLOWED TO TALK TO EACH OTHER ANY MORE...

COPPA COFFEE

**Alex** PEATTIE + TAYLOR

DARLING, I'M SO LOOKING FORWARD TO OUR HONEYMOON...!

CHECK IN 12

JUST MARRIED

ME TOO. I'M DELIRIOUSLY HAPPY...!

WHEN I BOOKED THE TICKETS SIX MONTHS AGO IT SEEMED SUCH AN UNREAL AND DISTANT PROSPECT. I COULDN'T ALLOW MYSELF TO BELIEVE IT WAS ACTUALLY GOING TO HAPPEN ONE DAY...

BUT NOW HERE WE ARE HAVING JUST DONE SOMETHING MAGICAL AND MARVELLOUS AND I THINK I MUST BE THE LUCKIEST MAN IN THE WORLD...!

SO WHERE ARE WE GOING? YOU'VE KEPT IT SECRET SO WELL...

HERE...

WHAT?! ANTIGUA? ISN'T THAT WHERE THE CRICKET IS?

AND WITH ENGLAND HAVING WON THEIR FIRST SERIES IN THE WEST INDIES SINCE 1968... IT'S A DREAM COME TRUE...

email: alex-cartoon@etgate.co.uk

57

**Alex** PEATTIE + TAYLOR

E-MAIL HAS REALLY CHANGED THE NATURE OF THE WAY WE FUND MANAGERS DEAL WITH BROKERS...

THESE DAYS THEY ARE ABLE TO ELECTRONICALLY SEND US THEIR IDEAS, WHICH WE ARE THEN FREE TO LOOK OVER AT A TIME OF OUR OWN CHOOSING

WHEREAS IN THE OLD DAYS THERE WAS NO OTHER OPTION THAN TO PHONE US DIRECTLY WHICH COULD EASILY BE AT A TIME WHICH WAS NOT CONVENIENT...

EXACTLY...

SIGH: AND IT WAS SO SATISFYING TO BE ABLE TO TELL THEM TO EFF OFF...

YES... KNOWING THAT THEY WERE SO DESPERATE FOR OUR BUSINESS THAT THEY COULDN'T AFFORD TO TAKE OFFENCE...

**Alex** PEATTIE + TAYLOR

WELL, GEORGIA, I'M MOVING TO A NEW JOB AND I'M BEING SENT ON THREE MONTHS GARDENING LEAVE...

AGAIN?!

I MUST SAY I THINK THAT MAKING BANKERS DO "GARDENING LEAVE" IS TOTALLY UNFAIR AND IN MY OPINION AMOUNTS TO NOTHING MORE THAN RESTRAINT OF TRADE...

I MEAN, WHY SHOULD A QUALIFIED PERSON BE OBLIGED TO WITHOLD THEIR PROFESSIONAL SKILLS MERELY AT THE PETTY-MINDED WHIM OF THEIR EMPLOYER?

ER, BUT, GEORGIA...

...IT'S MY GARDEN AND I CAN DO IT MYSELF IF I WANT TO...

WHAT ABOUT ME - YOUR GARDENER? WHAT AM I SUPPOSED TO DO?

**Alex** PEATTIE + TAYLOR

DAVID FOTHERINGHAM, THE CHAIRMAN OF THE SWAPS CHARITY BALL, HAS ASKED ME TO BE ON THE COMMITTEE THIS YEAR.

SINCE I LOST MY JOB MY CONFIDENCE HAS BEEN AT A REAL LOW EBB BUT THIS NEWS HAS GIVEN MY SELF-ESTEEM A BIG BOOST...

IT'LL BE A GOOD CHANCE FOR ME TO NETWORK WITH OTHER BANKERS, BUT MORE IMPORTANTLY IT SHOWS THAT DAVID HAS REAL FAITH IN MY ABILITY TO BOUNCE BACK...

SO, DAVID, YOU'RE GETTING CLIVE TO DO THE SEATING PLAN?

WELL, AS HE'S UNLIKELY EVER TO WORK AGAIN IT WON'T MATTER IF HE ALIENATES WHICHEVER BANK HE SEATS AT THE BACK BY THE LOOS...

**Alex** PEATTIE + TAYLOR

PROVIDING MEMBERS OF THE TEAM WITH A BLACKBERRY IS SUPPOSED TO ENHANCE THE WAY WE DO OUR JOBS...

FOR EXAMPLE IT ALLOWS YOU TO ACCESS YOUR E-MAIL WHEN OUT OF THE OFFICE AND THUS KEEP ABREAST OF YOUR INBOX AT THE WEEKEND...

HOWEVER IN VIEW OF A CONVERSATION I'VE JUST HAD WITH A CLIENT I'M GOING TO HAVE TO DISCIPLINE YOU FOR FAILURE TO MAKE PROPER USE OF THIS FACILITY...

YOU REPLIED TO AN E-MAIL ON SUNDAY? THIS SETS A DANGEROUS PRECEDENT... THEY'LL EXPECT US ALL TO BE ON HAND 24/7 NOW...

OOPS.

email: alex-cartoon@etgate.co.uk

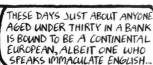

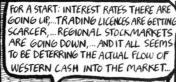

# Also available from Masterley Publishing

**The Best of Alex 1998 - 2001**

Boom to bust via the dotcom bubble.
£9.99 plus p+p

**The Best of Alex 2002**

Scandals rock the corporate world.
£9.99 plus p+p

**The Best of Alex 2003**

Alex gets made redundant.
£9.99 plus p+p

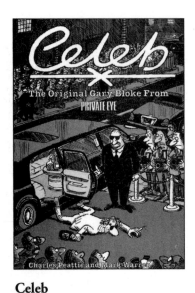

**Celeb**

Rock'n'roll excess with Gary Bloke.
£9.99 plus p+p

**The Alex Technique**

Alex's guide to survival in the City.
£7.99 plus p+p

**Son of Alex (1990)**

From our vaults:
Alex and fatherhood.
£4.99 plus p+p

## Cartoon Originals and Prints

The Alex and Celeb cartoon strip originals are all for sale. A strip measures 4 x 14 inches. If there's a particular one you want, phone or email us some information about it (the date it appeared, what the punch line was etc.) and we'll let you know if we still have it. If the original is not available, or you are too mean to purchase it, we can make a print of it for you. Originals and prints are signed by the creators.

For further details on prices and delivery charges for books or cartoons please contact

Alex
PO Box 39447
London
N10 3WA

Tel: 020 8374 1225
Fax: 0871 750 2343
Email: alex-cartoon@etgate.co.uk
Web: www.alexcartoon.com